The Little White Hen

Story by Beverley Randell   Illustrations by Isabel Lowe

The little white hen said,

"Today I am going

to lay an egg.

Where will I lay my egg?"

4

"You can lay your egg in here,"
said the big hens.
"We all lay eggs
inside the hen house."

"No," said the little white hen.
"I am going to lay my egg
outside the hen house."

Away went the little white hen.

She went into the grass.

"I will lay my egg
down here,"
said the little white hen.
"Oh, no!
Here comes a dog."

Away went the little white hen.

She went up on the roof.

"I will lay my egg

up here,"

said the little white hen.

"Oh, no!

Here comes a cat."

"Where can I lay my egg?"
said the little white hen.
"It is not safe for me
to lay my egg outside."

She looked down
at the hen house.

"I will lay my egg
inside with the hens, after all,"
said the little white hen.